Guitar Duets

Initial-Grade 3
for Trinity Guildhall examinations

2010-2015

Published by:
Trinity College London
89 Albert Embankment
London SE1 7TP UK

T +44 (0)20 7820 6100
F +44 (0)20 7820 6161
E music@trinityguildhall.co.uk
www.trinityguildhall.co.uk

Printed in England by Halstan & Co. Ltd, Amersham, Bucks.

What then is Love?

arr. Charles Duncan

Philip Rosseter
(1575-1623)

Winter

arr. Nicholas Powlesland

Antonio Vivaldi
(1678-1741)

Allegro

arr. Charles Duncan

Wolfgang Amadeus Mozart
(1756–1791)

Si la noche haze escura

Lee Sollory
(born 1959)

Majorca

John Compton

Dreamcatcher

Nick Powlesland

Menuet

Jean-Baptiste Lully
(1632-1687)

Mateixas d'es Figueral

arr. Jonathan Preiss

Traditional Mallorcan

Mareta, Mareta

arr. Eythor Thorlaksson

Folk song from Valencia

Old French Song

op. 39 no. 16

arr. Lee Sollory

Piotr Tchaikovsky
(1840–1893)

Hayride

Roger Winfield

Reproduced from *Tunes For Two, Book 3: 10 More Duets for Classical Guitar* by Roger Winfield. www.starbornbooks.co.uk

El Caballo

Roger Montgomery
(born 1947)

Tedesca

arr. Lee Sollory

Franz Joseph Haydn
(1732-1809)

Lezione

arr. Lee Sollory

Ferdinando Carulli
(1770-1841)

Acordai Doncela

arr. Yvon Rivoal

Traditional Brazilian

Canción de cuna

Lullaby

Jonathan Preiss
(born 1971)

Rondo

arr. Jonathan Preiss

Wolfgang Amadeus Mozart
(1756–1791)

Valse
op. 44 no. 1

Fernando Sor
(1778-1839)

Marchinha de carnaval

Celso Machado
(born 1953)

Danza Andaluza

Lee Sollory
(born 1959)